by Diana Noonan
illustrated by Vasja Koman

SCHOOL PUBLISHERS

Printed in Mexico

ISBN 10: 0-15-350643-1
ISBN 13: 978-0-15-350643-7

Ordering Options
ISBN 10: 0-15-350599-0 (Grade 2 On-Level Collection)
ISBN 13: 978-0-15-350599-7 (Grade 2 On-Level Collection)
ISBN 10: 0-15-357824-6 (package of 5)
ISBN 13: 978-0-15-357824-3 (package of 5)

2 3 4 5 6 7 8 9 10   050   15 14 13 12 11 10 09 08 07

Characters

Narrator 1

Narrator 2

Patrol Leader

Patroller 1

Patroller 2

Setting: A mountain Ski Patrol Station

3

Narrator 1: Do you have any idea what it's like to be caught in an avalanche? That is when lots of snow slides down the mountain.

Narrator 2: What would it feel like to lose your way in a blizzard?

Narrator 1: Today we are high up at Mount Cougar Ski Patrol Station. We are going to learn what the Ski Patrol does and why people need it.

Patrol Leader: Hello. Today the weather is clear, but there is still the chance of an avalanche. Some of the Ski Patrol are already coming down the mountain. They are putting out flags. The flags tell people to stay away from dangerous places.

Narrator 2: Could you tell us about your job please?

Patroller 1: Sure. I'm not a doctor, though I do understand enough about first aid to give help. If there is a problem on the mountain, I'm the person who is called.

Patroller 2: I help with first aid, too.

Narrator 1: What other jobs does the Ski Patrol do?

Patrol Leader: In a blizzard, the Ski Patrol moves people off the mountain.

Patroller 1: There are enough of us to check all the trails. We help people down if they have lost their way.

Patroller 2: We wear bright coats so people can see us in the snow.

Patroller 1: All skiers should wear bright clothes.

Narrator 2: What if there is an avalanche?

Patrol Leader: That happened not long ago. There were two people trapped in the snow.

Narrator 1: How did you find the people?

Patrol Leader: We are specially trained to work with dogs to help find people trapped in the snow.

Patroller 1: First of all, we find where the people are trapped.

Patroller 2: Then we work to dig them out quickly.

Narrator 1: What's the busiest time of day for a Ski Patrol team?

Patrol Leader: Mornings and nights are very busy. In the morning, we have to check the mountain to make sure that the trails are safe. We put out signs and flags to tell skiers about dangers.

13

Patroller 1: At night, we have to make sure that every last person is safely down from the mountain. We check far and wide to make sure that no one is lost or hurt.

Patroller 2: When every person is down, our work is done for the day. Then we can rest!

14

Think Critically

1. Why were the narrators at the Mount Cougar Ski Patrol Station?

2. Why do the patrollers put out flags?

3. Why do you think all skiers should wear bright clothes?

4. After you read page 5, did you think there would be an avalanche in the story? Why or why not?

5. How did you feel when you read about people trapped in the avalanche?

 **Social Studies**

Write a Paragraph Write a paragraph about why ski patrollers are important.

School-Home Connection Talk about the book with family members. Then talk about whether they would like to go skiing.

Word Count: 419